Hayley Newman is a perform
fiction and documentary pract
collectively around the curren
and is a member of the banc
musical Café Carbon was tak
Summit 2009. She is a tutor on t
at the Slade School of Fine Art.

...dies programme

Common is typeset in Figgins Sans by Nick Shinn. Named after
the Figgins foundry – inventor of the term sans serif – Figgins
Sans is a modern revival of the ubiquitous lettering found in 19th
century London.

**COMMON
HAYLEY NEWMAN**

Copy Press

The Copy Press Limited
51 South Street
Ventnor
Isle of Wight
PO38 1NG

copypress.co.uk

Commune no. 4
Editor: Vit Hopley
Reader: Yve Lomax
Copy-editor: Sara Peacock
Design: Amerang

Front cover © Hayley Newman

Printed on Munken Print White
no.18 80gsm. Munken Print White
standard products are FSCTM
and PEFC certified.
Printed and bound in England.

First edition © Copy Press Ltd/
Hayley Newman, 2013

Hayley Newman asserts the moral
right to be identified as the author of
this work.

A catalogue record for this book is
available from the British Library

ISBN-13 978-0-9553792-6-0
ISBN-10 0-9553792-6-1

CONTENTS

PROLOGUE

One dark winter's night, while cycling home through the City of London, I was stopped by something powerful, a force that existed beyond my own free will.[1] The four traffic lights at the intersection between London Wall and Bishopsgate were glowing red. I took this as a warning sign to beware and stay away from the dangerous and putrid creatures of the night, the metallic four-wheeler monsters that were pulsating and spewing out their poisonous smoke.[2] Then out of the darkness a fright of ghostly beings slid along the road toward me. Frozen and enthralled I did not move, I could not move; they had stilled all motion. There were hundreds of them. Loosely connected, they slowly and deliberately staggered into the space normally occupied by the metallic four-wheelers.

The ghosts were carrying large white squares with letters on them; I saw H on one and N on another. My initials? My brain felt scrambled. The group in front of me was unfamiliar yet reminded me of something, and as I looked around I saw other figures. Lurking on the pavement next to me were moody shadows with black and blue stripes hung heavily over their lumbering bodies.

The spectral crowd began to place their giant white squares on the road and lie beside them. I was imagining them resting

1 ... The City of London ... A small area within Greater London ... Boundaries remain unchanged since the middle ages ... Otherwise known as the City or The Square Mile ... The City of London vies with New York to be financial capital of the world ...
2 ... London Wall and Bishopsgate ... Two roads that intersect in the northeast of the City of London ...

before continuing their epic and endless journey, when my thoughts were interrupted by the approach of a four-wheeler with a blue flashing light. My heart started beating fast. I tried to shout 'watch out', but the words didn't come. Stuck and silent, they stayed lodged in the glottis of my throat. No one else seemed worried, and my response and immediate sense of danger left me feeling foolish. Before long they began chanting. 'Do coo nuts! So foo tuts! Bo do guts! Go ho muts!' I couldn't make sense of it. What were they trying to tell me? Us? I was sure they had a message but felt disconnected from the scene unravelling before me.

A tap on my shoulder brought me back to the present. So immersed in this world of ghouls I hadn't seen my old friend C next to me. I took off my earmuffs and put on my glasses; she looked great – she always looked great. We greeted each other with a kiss and a bit of small talk before turning back to watch the event before us. As I turned I heard their words clearly for the first time that evening. 'No to cuts! No to cuts! No to cuts!' Glasses on, I looked at the group lying in the road. They were wearing scrubs: blue, cotton tops and trousers. The white squares were no longer random letters but placards that read: UNISON, NHS, STOP ALL THE CUTS, FIGHT FOR EVERY JOB! THEY SAY CUT TAX, WE SAY PAY TAX![3]

This was a protest, a spectacular protest and not a spectre. A real 'die in'. It was nurses, doctors, trade unionists and NHS patients, and not a gaggle of ghoulish zombies, who had managed to stop the traffic at the intersection for a near-death five minutes. They were protesting against cuts to the National Health Service.[4]

During my revelation I heard a City worker commenting,

3 ... 9 March 2011 ... Day X for the NHS ... Mass demo to keep the NHS public takes place in the City of London ... Nurses, doctors, trade unionists and patients march from the Royal London Hospital to St Bartholomew's Hospital ... Health workers lie down in the middle of road and stage a 'die in' against cuts to services ...
4 ... 12 July 2010 ... White paper 'Equity and Excellence: Liberating the NHS' proposes extensive reorganization ... NHS reform happening in England only ... British Medical Association and Royal College of Nursing remain opposed to reforms ... Healthcare not compatible with free-market models ... Reforms are privatization by the back door ... No mention of proposed changes made by government in election manifesto ...

'the police should water-cannon them'.[5] Turning, I followed him with my eyes, stared and mouthed a heated word, as white-hot tears of injustice ran down my cheeks. The thought of NHS staff fighting cuts to a national heath service being punished in any way, let alone such a brutal and inhuman one, left me feeling speechless. How could someone say such a thing? It was at that moment I made my decision. I would go in, undercover ... let me introduce myself:

Self-appointed Artist-in-Residence
City of London

Hayley Newman

**The Square Mile
London**

5 ... Home Secretary Theresa May rules out use of water cannons at student protests ... Scotland Yard public order branch Commander says it would be foolish not to consider their use ...

EARLY BIRD

My alarm rings: it is 4.30am. I can hear the birds singing and it is starting to get light. I get up, shower and have some breakfast before packing a bag for my first day as 'Self-Appointed Artist-in-Residence' in the City of London. The City of London is close to my home. I can see its skyline from my kitchen window.

Why 'Self-Appointed Artist-in-Residence?' you may ask. A deliberate ploy not to be beholden to any form of power, financial or other, I might answer. Being employed by the City or a bank to act as an artist-in-residence would not be an equal relationship.[1] By self-appointing I give myself agency to act independently of the City and its inherent values.

A self-appointed artist needs tools, so I pack a digital camera, MP3 recorder, sketchpad, pencils, a set of watercolours, some sandwiches, a flask and a dress, just in case. I bicycle the half mile from my flat in Whitechapel to the City of London. By 5.34am I am outside the Royal Exchange with just two minutes to spare before sunrise.[2] While I wait for the sun to rise nothing much happens. Lazy. This is dawn: a mixture of pink and yellow artificial streetlight with an azure blue sky, the ratio of which constantly changes until daylight is reached.

I am very keen to get started in my new job, but find that I am not alone. There are other people here in my square mile of

1 ... Deutsche Bank owns one of the world's largest corporate art collections ... Over 56,000 works of art in collection ... Royal Bank of Scotland thought to own largest corporate art collection in Britain ... Sponsoring art and maintaining collections aligns banks with elite culture ...
2 ... The current Royal Exchange is third on site ... Originally a centre of commerce for the City ... Now a luxury shopping centre ...

prime studio.[3] Van drivers are parked and making deliveries of anything from toiletries to food. Security guards and cleaners make up the rest of the population. An equal mix of male and female, this predominantly migrant workforce invisibly protects and cleans the offices, stairwells and atriums for a minimum wage.[4] By 7am these service industry workers are already on their way home as most City workers begin to arrive. On the streets a clear economic division of labour between the poorly and excessively paid reveals itself.[5]

Looking down at the pavement, I see insects. Crepuscular friends twitching their claws and wings in the dawn, preparing for a new day. According to a very quick pseudo-calculation based on the square metre of ground in front of me, the number of insects in the City of London could easily match its work-force. Many of the insects here are members of the resistance; they shadow and spy on traders day and night. It is commonly thought that the best spies in the insect world are the earwigs and spiders; butterflies are the most farsighted, but their flam-boyant wings are a disadvantage and often give them away.

The insect spies' most important assets are antennae, wings and compound eyes. Other insect/spy skills include stinging, biting and cutting. Those living in colonies are the most self-organized. Being killed by fly sprays, swatted or eaten by another insect are some of the risks insect spies face on a daily basis and, because of this, they often die before being debriefed.

Insects use a system of buzzwords learnt from the banking sector to communicate important information. Key phrases include: debug, long tail and cockroach problem. Cockroach problem is my favourite as it describes a situation where one piece of bad news is followed by even more bad news. Like having cockroaches, a company with a cockroach problem can always expect more bad news to turn up shortly.

3 ... In 2011 average office space rental is £56 per square foot ... City of London home to 75 million square feet of office space ... More skyscrapers being built ...
4 ... Minimum wage for workers aged 21 and over is £6.08 per hour in 2011 ... Bankers' bonuses in same year expected to total £7bn ...
5 ... Debate about pay ratio needed ... Evidence sought to justify high pay ... Maximum bottom-to-top pay levels need to be set ...

Barely visible to the eye, the insects know how to make their way around the Square Mile undetected: flying into board-rooms, crawling into offices through air vents and hiding inside bags and coats. Have you ever heard the expression 'fly on the wall' and wondered where it came from? Here of course! Some insects possess natural stripes, which help them achieve even more anonymity here in the City.

The insect resistance is a rapidly growing movement. Recently three million insects took part in a biodiversity demon-stration outside the London Stock Exchange to protest against the installation of beehives on its roof.[6] The insects were not protesting against the hives, but the hypocrisy behind the kind of corporate social responsibility that superficially points toward supporting biodiversity while carrying on with a 'busi-ness as usual' approach and killing our planet through continued investment in unsustainable industries.[7]

The insects saw putting hives on the roof of the London Stock Exchange as a cheap publicity stunt. They wanted fundamental change. The demonstration was described in the local press as an 'infestation'. If only the journalist had brought a magnifying glass with her she would have seen millions of flies with placards that read FLIES AGAINST ECOCIDE, GRASS-HOPPERS AGAINST GREENWASH, and she would have seen bees carrying hand-painted signs saying, MAKE HONEY NOT MONEY.

A more conspicuously revered City population is to be found in the elevated statues of famous men looking down on passers-by. Nearly all the public statues of important figures here are of white men. There are few ethnic minorities or women of dis-tinction memorialized apart from queens and allegorical female forms such as Britannia, Venus and Justice. While semi-naked women look out dreamily from porticos on the tops of buildings

6 ... Biodiversity reaches point of no return ... Ecosystems can no longer be plundered ... August 2011 London Stock Exchange welcomes new worker drones to their roof ... Honey to be given as corporate gifts ... Local people will benefit from training ...

7 ... Corporate conscience, corporate citizenship, sustainably responsible business ... Corporate social responsibility (CSR) is just public relations ... CSR seen as part of companies' long-term strategies ... Helps build value, gain contracts and attract ethical consumers ... Companies often promote CSR while following radically different policies ...

their male counterparts are sitting, standing and riding above the heads of passers-by. Wearing cloaks, wigs and hats they carry impressive titles such as Duke, Sir, Lord and King.

I recently came across the infamous statue of Margaret Thatcher (Britain's first female prime minister and Conservative Party leader) in the Guildhall Art Gallery. The larger than life white marble statue of Thatcher was decapitated by Paul Kelleher in 2002.[8] It is now housed in a perspex box to prevent further attacks.

Insects, cleaners and statues populate the early morning City. Statues occupy space as the dead made visible, while cleaners are given supporting roles as the invisible living.

I begin to take photographs of doorways, bins, street corners, shops and flowers. Immediately I am followed into an alleyway. Is he a security guard? My heart beats fast. I need to get out of the labyrinth as quickly as I can. I am reminded that this is a state within a state with its own police force, its own mayor, and where business is its king and everything I can see around me belongs to someone else.[9][10]

The City waits for three hundred thousand workers to horizontally and vertically fill its offices, shops, bars, libraries, cafes and streets. I wait for the deadening silence, emptiness and quiet to end.

8 ... Theatre producer attacks £150,000 statue ... Artwork will never be same again ... Police told 'I think it looks better like that.' ...
9 ... The Lord Mayor of the City of London is not elected like the Mayor of London ... The City of London Corporation has its own bespoke police force ... The Corporation's privately funded functions are exempt from freedom of information legislation ...
10 ... Private land in the City of London includes: all the park and garden areas, churches and gardens, Paternoster Square, the Barbican Centre and Barbican Estate, Smithfield Market, Leadenhall Market, Museum of London, Broadgate Estate, Network Rail Stations, London Underground Stations, New Street Square, Aviva Square, Inner and Middle Temple, forecourt areas and squares attached to buildings (such as St Paul's Cathedral) as well as all the Bridges in the City (Tower Bridge, London Bridge, Southwark Bridge, Millennium Bridge and Blackfriars Bridge) ...

EARLY BIRD

A TANGIBLE MOMENT

I am at St Bartholomew's hospital, which I first visited 30 years ago. It is old and decrepit now; peeling paint on window frames flakes around unwashed windows, and vents pump warm stale air onto the streets.[1] With the hospital in front of me, the past has suddenly become tangible. Memories of my time here start to come back, not all together and not all at once: I am feeling my past in the present and I am no longer afraid.

The memories make me feel different and strange as they move through my body. You know what happens don't you? Seeing a visual cue you feel the feelings, but the feelings don't have words – well, not in the first instance. While reconnecting these feelings with memories I spontaneously recollect practising how to walk on a balcony at the back of this building. Remembering the pain of one small step after another I wonder if the balcony is still there. Is my memory real? I look and I am not disappointed. It is there. I am relieved to have found a tangible connection to the past; it did happen here and my memory does work. I haven't thought about that day for a very long time.

Of course, I always knew the building was here. I have walked past it many times, but I never looked up. Knowing was enough as I chose to ignore its dumb, white façade. Now, I am outside looking in through the tops of misted ground-floor windows. I

1 ... February 2011 ... Barts and the Royal London Hospital trust to cut 635 jobs over next two years ... Nearly 10 per cent of nursing posts to go ... Trust currently cares for over 900,000 people annually ... Trust aims to save £56 million over two years ... Royal London Hospital about to open largest hospital in Europe ... Built as part of a £1 billion private finance initiative ... Total repayment £5.3 billion ... The contract will last until 2048 ...

see cupboard corners, dusty pipes and yellowish paint: these are the hospital service rooms for laundry, cleaning stuff, equipment and boilers.

My feet take me to the side of the building. I enter. It is 6.30am and there is no one else here. I walk up the stairs to the third floor. This is where I was taken; I remember the name of the ward and realize that I know the address by heart.[2] This is where I screamed the word morphine and then felt no relief whatsoever.

2 ... Both the City of London and hospitals have wards ... I was in the W G Grace ward at Barts Hospital ... There are 25 wards in the City of London ... Barts Hospital is in the ward of Farringdon Without ...

A TANGIBLE MOMENT

FROTTAGE IN THE CITY

I walk to Bank underground station.[1] It is the rush hour and I am about to jam myself between crowds of people as they surge down the streets to work. I want to pass myself off as a City worker, so as to make a physical connection with the people who work here.

Hanging around the station exits, I wait for waves of people to pour out. I join them. Unnoticed, I flow with the crowd. Staying with the pace, I walk faster, then slower, then faster. Emboldened by my anonymity and the security of being surrounded by others, I get close enough to touch people. Not flesh, but a sleeve, a cuff or the corner of a jacket. Touching people, feeling their clothes, getting close enough first to sense, then smell.

The woman in front of me has a ponytail that is caught on the material of her jacket and is splayed out across the width of her back. Reaching out with my hand I touch the edge of her olive coloured coat; it is slightly rough, but good quality. I'm close enough to see its weave and the stitching on its cuff.

If you have ever tried looking at the ground while walking in a crowd you will know that it is vertiginous; hundreds of shoes moving at random, outside the control of the bodies above them. At this pace feet move too fast to be seen as anything other than a blur. Most of the footwear is dark: black or brown.

1 ... 96,000 passengers use Bank underground station during peak time ... One of the largest underground rail complexes in the world ... Bank station links Central, Waterloo and City, District and Circle lines as well as the Docklands Light Railway ... Docklands Light Railway connects the City of London and Canary Wharf ...

Our collective noise is a combination of swishing, stomping and clattering.

I catch a glimpse of my hair as I pass a shop window. I look ragged despite wearing my best clothes. Seeing myself I realize how important it is for me to pass. For now I need to remain invisible, just another banker, office worker, or shop assistant on my way to work.

Different pavement widths bring the crowd together in alternative ways. The narrow paths squeeze us into a line, while the wider ones allow us to fill the whole pavement. Varying my position in the crowd, I hang back and then push into the group, letting myself be caught in its slip-stream. I remain at the back of the crowd for a time. Moving into its middle, I hold my position and wait obstinately for people to move aside. As a group we are more cohesive: we cross roads, stop traffic and make others move aside as we pass. But eventually, as our numbers dwindle, we become weaker and loose our momentum and mass. We are now fewer and since we can't be called a crowd any more we transform back into a loose group of individuals.

As the group starts to disperse, I turn 180 degrees and walk back into the flow of people out of which I have come. I walk back to the station, through the middle of the crowd. Now I can see people's faces as they think, frown, concentrate, smile or daydream. I see their anger, frustration and bitterness alongside their boredom and kindness. The experience of walking back through the crowd is more abrasive than walking with the group, and holding my position in the centre is difficult to maintain. More often than not, I find myself at the crowd's edge taking the route of least resistance back to the station, before picking up another group and beginning the process again.

Looking up at a nearby clock, I see that it is 9.30am. The rush hour is over and my work is done for now.

FROTTAGE IN THE CITY

LIFE SAVER

Characters

HALF A TON
SCORE
TENNER
LADY GODIVA
NUGGET
QUID
FIFTY PENCE
TWENTY PENCE
TEN PENCE
FIVE PENCE
TUPPENCE
PENNY
HOVERFLY
LADYBIRD

Scene

The action takes place in a bank safe deposit box.

ACT 1

A HOVERFLY flies into a bank. Sounds like the beginning of a joke, doesn't it? She is shadowing a trader who has taken a detour into a high-street bank to cash a cheque. Bored, the HOVERFLY sits on the top right-hand corner of a very large computer screen. Just below her, the time reads a digital 10.30am. Restless, she buzzes into an open box in the corner of the room. Before she can fly out, the door is shut behind her with a thud.

[*It is dark. The characters can be heard but barely seen. They are only identifiable as shadows. They are not aware of* HOVERFLY'S *presence and only the audience can hear her. A key turns in a lock.*]

TENNER [*whining*]: Let me out! I want to get out of here!

TUPPENCE: He is having a panic attack, give him some space.

TENNER: I can't breathe. I need water.

TUPPENCE [*soothing* TENNER]: Breathe in for the count of four and out for the count of six.

HOVERFLY [*takes note of where she is*]: Pitch black.

TENNER: I can't stand it.

SCORE: We've been in this place for too long.

FIFTY PENCE: This is an ethical bank... [*reflectively*] What is ethical about keeping us in these cramped conditions?[1]

HOVERFLY [*realising she is trapped*]: I may not get out of this situation alive. Perhaps now is a good time to lay the eggs I am carrying?

HALF A TON: What has this bank ever done for us? Nothing happens, there's no interest in savings any more.[2]

---

1 ... Number of people moving accounts to ethical banks, credit unions and mutual building societies rising ... Current high-street banks at risk of becoming a mono-culture ... High-street banks with corporate social responsibility mandates criticized for investments in arms, fossil fuels and use of tax havens ...
2 ... Savers lose out on interest repayment downturn ... Borrowers save money on repayments ... Savings income lost while borrowers gain due to low interest rates ...

LADY GODIVA: We have been here for five years. [LADY GODIVA *sits, fanning herself calmly.*]

HALF A TON: Every month it's the same. They open the door and bring in new ones.

[HOVERFLY *sits on* PENNY *and remembers the flowers she spent time collecting nectar from, just before she mated in midair.*]

SCORE [*angrily*]: I am worth less than I was last year. I have been devalued because of you. [*He points at* TENNER.][3]

TENNER: I am trapped too. I could be out in the world, transforming, reproducing, making more money.[4]

PENNY: I am just a penny, but I'm still 1/2,000 of you, and Tenner I am 1/1,000 of you.

LADY GODIVA [*in a Zen-like state*]: We are all connected.

[HOVERFLY flies to the back of the safe to find a place to lay her eggs. She knows that she needs to lay them soon.]

FIVE PENCE: Why so grumpy today, Score?

SCORE: We are worth less because of … him. [SCORE *grudgingly points at* TENNER.] They should go back to where they came from.

HOVERFLY [*lands on* HALF A TON]: This looks like a safe place to lay my eggs. [*She begins to squeeze*] Push, push, push…

HALF A TON: I want to party and to make tons more money for the sake of it.

TUPPENCE: Why so crude?

HALF A TON: What's wrong with wanting more?

FIVE PENCE [*smiles to himself*]: Let's arrange our own heist.

---

3 … Quantitative easing tried for first time in UK … First round introduced in March 2009 … Money made available electronically … More quantitative easing on its way …

4 … Consumer spending used as economic indicator … Consumer spending over next decade predicted to be subdued …

HOVERFLY: I can't breathe; I don't know if I can last.

TEN PENCE: What about our plans to finance micro-funds in India?

LADY GODIVA: We can work in so many ways to get what we want: buy food, diamonds or people. We make wars happen and cause poverty. We also help feed, clothe and house people.

HALF A TON: I just want to be carried around in a pocket and then be transferred to another pocket.

LADY GODIVA: They used a friend of mine to pay off a policeman a few months ago. She was put into a brown envelope before being handed over.

HOVERFLY [*mutters to herself*]: Focus on their conversation or imagine yourself in a meadow. [*Having laid her eggs* HOVERFLY *is now slumped in one of the back corners of the safe.*]

SCORE: I was transferred electronically to a bank account in the Cayman Islands.[5] If you ask me, what is done with us is not our responsibility.

PENNY: You belonged to a tax avoider?[6]

SCORE: It was really impersonal, millions of us jostling for the attention of our owners.

TENNER: I've heard of the taxman. A bogeyman right?

HOVERFLY [*desperately*]: Air, give me air.

FIFTY PENCE: I want to save the planet. Instead, I am just a saving.

PENNY: Our owner is saving us for a rainy day, a bit of security in case she needs us, and nothing more.

HOVERFLY [*crawls over the piled-up money*]: I am dying.

---

5 ... Twenty of Britain's largest companies operate subsidiaries in tax havens ... Companies include: Royal Dutch Shell, BP, Lloyds Banking Group, Tesco, HSBC, Vodafone Group and Barclays ...
6 ... In 2011 UK Uncut protestors shut down Vodafone shops across the country ... Protestors want £6bn back in evaded taxes ... Vodaphone settle dispute by paying £1.25bn ... Government deny big corporations receive preferential treatment from tax authorities ...

HALF A TON [*experiencing a very enjoyable memory*]: I had a brilliant holiday in the City of London last year.

HOVERFLY: Need to rest – no more energy.

QUID: Was that the time when you made friends with the fake banknote?[7]

NUGGET [*indignantly*]: It wasn't Half a Ton who did that, it that was me.

HOVERFLY: I'll just sit here on this coin.

TEN PENCE: Have you ever been in debt?

HOVERFLY [*barely audible*]: Goodbye world, goodbye my future children.

NUGGET: When we were kids, my uncle and aunt were taken away.

HOVERFLY: Good ...b ...y ... .[*Her words drift into silence.*]

PENNY: You know we don't really exist? No one has ever seen us; we are not tangible.[8] We are smoke and mirrors, sleight of hand, magic… and because of that…

HOVERFLY: Hhhh ... [*At the exact moment* HOVERFLY *breathes her last breath a* LADYBIRD *creeps out from the recesses of the safe and eats her.*]

CURTAIN

---

7 ... One note in every 5,000 fake ... Pound coins most common forgeries ...
8 ... Physical cash accounts for less than 3 per cent of total money stock ...

DAYLIGHT RUBBERY

Let me introduce myself: I am a Bank Rubber. No, not a bank robber like those bonus-busting hypocrites, I am a Bank Rubber. I have got a graphite block, paper and masking tape, and I'm ready to rub the banks. Up and down, from side to side. That's rubbing, not robbing.

I have made detailed plans for a series of bank rubbings to begin at 11.30am this morning. I intend to make rubbings of the fronts and insides of banks including doors, tables and fixtures. Their random marks will be expressed on a page.

I am starting with Lloyds Bank on Threadneedle Street. Lloyds was one of the banks rescued by the government in 2008 and, to be completely honest with you, it has not got a great record.[1] It has been accused of money laundering and encouraging customers to commit tax evasion, as well as making loans to arms manufacturers and mis-selling bonds. With 40 per cent of it owned by the public, could Lloyds be a prime target for daylight rubbery?

I take out my graphite block, place a sheet of paper on the wall and fix it to its place with masking tape. I begin to rub the outside walls of the bank first. Left to right and right to left, my hand moves rapidly across the white sheet. As I rub, the motion of the graphite block draws out shadowy images, which appear on the sheet of paper. Next, I begin to rub the brass plates on the front of the building, but I soon realize I am in full view of the

1 ... Lloyds received a £17bn government bailout in 2008 ... Lloyds Banking Group plc was formed through the acquisition of HBOS and Lloyd's TSB in 2009 ... Taxpayers own 40 per cent of the bank ...

bank assistants working inside. I need to make a quick choice: do I continue with my rubbings and get moved on, or do I see if the system can accommodate my request to rub a partially nationalized bank?

Putting on an air of innocence, I enter the bank and ask permission to make some brass rubbings of the front of the building. The assistant is concerned and asks the manager, who is also concerned and suggests calling central office, who say no. The assistant helpfully suggests that I come back and do some rubbings in the evening or at the weekend, which is exactly what I was thinking.

Daylight rubbery was always going to be difficult on a weekday between nine and five, so I move on to rub a derelict Iraqi bank. While I am making a rubbing of the brass plaque on its façade, a well-dressed man approaches me asking if I know the meaning of the Arabic word مصرف الرافدين, which I have just rubbed. I say I don't, but imagine it to be the name of the bank itself, 'Rafidain'.[2] Continuing the conversation, he asks what I am doing. I reply that I am an artist-in-residence making bank rubbings for a project. (Note to self: always drop the self-appointed prefix when it is to your advantage.) He points to the Lloyd's Building, 'Do you know the name of that building and who designed it?'[3] 'It's the Lloyd's Building by Richard Rogers', I answer. Unexpectedly he hands me his card, saying that if I ever want to visit Lloyd's of London he will happily be my host.

'By the way', he adds, waving his arm in my general direction 'you will need to be better dressed than that to get into the building.'

2 ... One of the largest and oldest banks in Iraq ... Middle East offices previously adorned with portraits of Saddam Hussein ... Sanctions forced Rafidian bank to close London branch in 1990 ... Bank blacklisted by UN in 1991 ...

3 ... Lloyd's of London not to be confused with Lloyds Bank ... Lloyd's of London is home to the British insurance and re-insurance market ... Alternatively known as the Inside Out Building ...

DAYLIGHT RUBBERY

LUNCH

Main Course
Credit Crunchies[1]

Ingredients
Hundreds and thousands of house loans
1 hedge of risky investments
1 cup of investment banking
2 tablespoons of oil
1 tonne of high profits and bonuses
1 teaspoon of stability
Billions in extra credit
1 handful of short-term policies

Pour hundreds and thousands of house loans into your food processor and pulse. Then slice, dice, structure and hedge risky investments before repackaging them with the offer of attractive returns. Take a cup of investment banking and fry in oil. Add some high profits and bonuses, boil down to reduce liquidity. Taste and leave to boom and bust. Grind some stability into small pieces and add to your existing stock. Next, take a large bowl, measure out a handful of short-term policies and fold in extra credit. This bail-out recipe is an acquired taste and may be hard to stomach.

1 ... August 2007 ... Severe shortage of money/credit grips world ... Governments pump billions into banks to restore liquidity ... UK customers withdraw £1bn from Northern Rock ... The biggest run on a British bank for more than a century ... August 2011 ... Business as usual ... Some banks back in profit ... Bonus culture back in favour ... Painful austerity measures still to come ... UK government moves to right ... 25 years of stagnation ahead ...

Desert
Eton Mess[2]

Ingredients
1 coalition government[3]
1 corrupt PR guru[4]
5 kg corruption warnings
1 tsp fake remorse
Prime cuts of heath service, forestry commission,
schools, transport and social security
$^{1}/_{2}$ bucket load of private investors
$^{1}/_{2}$ bucket load of tax cuts
1 education system
Thousands of students
A very long recession
Kilos of indifference and arrogance

To begin, fold a coalition government to establish the power base for this recipe. Next, take a corrupt PR guru, separate out warnings of corruption, and half-bake his departure with a basting of fake remorse. Harvest prime cuts from the health service, forestry commission, schools, transport and social security before boiling down and reducing to a tepid sludge. Quickly pour a bucket load of private investors and tax cuts into the mix. Next, take the education system, grind it to a pulp and batter the students into submission. Steam a long recession before adding kilos of indifference to multiculturalism, human rights, poverty and inequality.

2 ... The Conservative Prime Minister David Cameron attended Eton College ...
3 ... May 2010 ... Conservatives and Liberal Democrats form coalition ... Colloquially known as the ConDems ... Deal includes action points on deficit reduction, banking reform, spending review (NHS and schools), tax, immigration, political reform, pensions and welfare, education, EU, civil liberties and the environment ...
4 ... January 2011 ... Conservative communications director Andy Coulson resigns in wake of News of the World phone hacking scandal ...

THE UNDERWRITING OF DISASTER

I arrange to meet the Lloyd's broker outside Rafidain Bank at 2pm. Transformed, I am wearing a grey silk dress and walking through Leadenhall Market with the broker, who is fixated on star signs and horoscopes.

Inside the Lloyd's Building, I am issued with a day pass by Kayley (a woman with a notably similar name to mine), which allows me access to the underwriting room and its concrete, glass, wood, marble and metal interior. As I walk across the marble floor I look up and see escalators zigzagging across the vertical space of the atrium, transporting brokers between floors. On the ground floor the dark wooden desks and tables that fill the underwriting room make it feel like a cross between a library, coffee shop and airline check-in. I see agents huddled at tables whispering to each other in hushed tones.

With an ambivalent wave of his arm the broker tells me that women have only been allowed on the floor for the past twelve years.

In the middle of the underwriting room the Lutine Bell, salvaged from a shipwreck, hangs inside a carved wooded rostrum. Originally tolled to mark the loss of a ship, it is now only rung to commemorate disasters of global significance such as tsunamis, bombings or royal deaths. This salvaged piece of metal, rung once for good news and twice for bad, is the focal point of the room.

Lloyd's originated in a coffee house of the same name, where men gathered to bet on odds for and against ships returning with their cargo. Lloyd's history is on display throughout the building and includes two open logbooks that are known as the Loss Books. The books record hundreds of years of disaster. Adjacent to each other, the book on the left is open at a page from two hundred years ago, while the one on the right holds accounts of recent disaster and lost lives. A ship sinks in Thailand in August 2011 another off the coast of Africa in August 1811. Each handwritten entry is filled out with an elaborate swish of pen and ink. Reading the words 'eleven dead' comes as an emotional shock and reminder that disaster is persistent. As the broker and I look at the entries in the logbooks he explains that the most important thing for insurers (and the rest of us, come to that) is to avoid death. I later find that many of the ships originally insured by Lloyd's were engaged in slave trading. Back then, the death of slaves would have meant loss of cargo to an insurer.

We take one of the external glass lifts to the eleventh floor. I'm interested in the verticality of the City: the status of the highest buildings; the spaces of privilege and power; the directors' offices, the boardrooms, the penthouses. As I go up and down I draw a mental graph that maps my occupation of its vertical space, and tracks my movements in lifts, on stairs and in escalators. Coincidently, the graph has begun to look like the rise and fall of stocks and shares.

The glass lifts are on the outside of the building alongside other utilities such as plumbing, heating and electrical cabling. What goes up must come down. I think about excrement flowing down the pipes before entering the sewage system beneath us. What would that look like on my graph? Crudely put, the privilege of shitting from a great height is only conferred on the most powerful.

Once at the top of the building, we visit the eighteenth-century Adam Room, a committee room that started its life as a Wiltshire dining room. The room was bought by Lloyd's in the 1950s, taken apart and transported to London where it was installed in their previous premises before being fully restored and placed in its current home within the 'inside-out' architecture of the Lloyd's Building.

As I look out of the Adam Room windows the view is no longer an English landscape or even the expected city skyline, but a metallic grid, the interior of the Lloyd's Building itself.

The broker takes me for tea at a nearby coffee shop. He suggests we go halves on a lottery ticket for the Euro Millions draw. I agree on the gamble. Insurers insist that gambling and insurance are not the same thing. Their rationale is that gambling embraces risk and insurance minimizes it. Risk remains a common factor in both gambling and insurance: loss and gain. He tells me he plays the lottery hoping to make a better life for his family. How much better does he need things to be?

We did not win.

Lloyd's of London not only insure homes, cars, oilrigs and celebrity legs, they also underwrite the weather: hurricanes, floods and tsunamis are all on their books. Lloyd's recently made a public statement about climate change, corporate social responsibility and the need to protect both the environment and the future of the insurance industry. Climate change is linked to the greater frequency of extreme weather, and the insurance industry is bracing itself for a new frontier of climate insurance, which will mean factoring climate change into risk models and making sure the industry continues to underwrite for profit. Writing in its 360° Risk Insight publication 'Climate Change and Security: Risks and Opportunities for Business', Lloyd's tell us 'Through research, reports, events, news and online content, Lloyd's 360° Risk Insight drives the global risk agenda as it takes shape. We provide practical advice that businesses need to turn risk into opportunity.'

Turning risk into opportunity, but for whom? Deepwater Horizon and Hurricane Katrina have cost billions of dollars. Deepwater Horizon was the worst environmental disaster in the history of the USA and the most costly manmade insurance loss since 9/11. Many of the costs for re-calibrating the insurance system will be passed on, but what about the corporations that have contributed to climate change through their polluting practices? Deepwater Horizon was a manmade disaster but was

Hurricane Katrina a manmade or natural disaster? Who is going to bear the actual cost of climate change and how will people most affected by climate change (those who are least likely to have contributed to it) be treated justly? What would happen if some natural disasters were re-categorized as manmade? Will corporations and governments who have chosen to ignore the climate science, and who continue to operate a 'business as usual' mandate, be asked to pay for the climate-related destruction they helped create?

THE UNDERWRITING OF DISASTER

THE LOBBY

I enter a lobby. Hollow, empty and quiet, muted in every possible way. I sit down on a black leather couch to the left of the entrance. A receptionist is sitting opposite. The large minimalist clock behind her is faceless. I think the time is 3.30pm. Remaining silent, I try not to be noticed as, even though I am dressed smartly, I have no business here.

I wait. But what am I waiting for? To be thrown out? No, for now, my only purpose is to wait. It is surprisingly pleasant. Every modern office block has a lobby and there are many different kinds: narrow, tall, thin, wide, wood panelled, crystalline. The lobby usually reflects the corporate standing and aspiration of the companies in the offices it serves. This one has its own security guard and receptionist, flower display, art, marble floor, leather couch and automatic door. I am experiencing pleasure as I continue to wait here. This is advanced business life, immaculate and pristine. I am waiting.

Taking out my notebook, I draw and make notes. My mind wanders and I begin to play a game. The game involves inventing names for buildings to inspire a new architectural vision for the City of London. Here goes:

The Cornetto
The Lunchbox
The Ghost
The Flasher
Le Zig-Zag

The Boob Tube
The Intestine
The Gekko (after Gordon)
The Overdraft
The Climax
The False Leg
The Dog's Dinner

Light floods into the front of the lobby, which is glass from floor to ceiling. It is a tantalizing space, full of anticipation and designed for awe. Everyone moves quietly. Coughing, sniffing, shuffling and a distant alarm are all amplified throughout. The sliding glass doors, which pulse open and shut even when there is no one here, swish when they open and squeak when they close, briefly letting in the sound of traffic only to mask it again. A cleaning lady wipes away the footprints of visitors as they pass through.

The receptionist looks over at me for a third time before getting up from her chair. As she approaches, she bends forward slightly to make her exceptionally polite, but nevertheless assertive, enquiry. 'Who are you waiting for?' she asks. 'Shirley Mudd,' I answer with the first name that comes to mind. 'You are in the wrong place; no one by that name works here,' she tells me.

I get up and walk to the doors, which quiver slightly before swishing open.

THE LOBBY

HEAVY METAL

I have come to the London Metal Exchange (LME) on Cornhill. The great thing about the LME is that, unlike the London Stock Exchange (LSX), the public can watch trading live, in action. I have booked a viewing slot at 4.15pm.

On arrival I am given a pass card to electronically swipe myself into the viewing gallery. From here I have a panoramic view of the traders; raised above the floor, I look down on trading through a set of windows. The gallery is sealed from the trading floor and, although viewers and traders can see each other, little can be heard.

Trading at the LME takes place in the middle of an inner ring of seats around which computer and phone terminals radiate outwards. The room has a concentric layout, similar to a cattle market in which trading happens in five-minute bouts known as 'rings'. Microphones hang in the air over the action, amplifying the excited voices of the traders as each fights to be heard above the rest. One man leans forward on the edge of his seat, while another stands, shoulders shrugged, a phone on each ear. At the periphery of the circle a woman makes hand signals; buying, selling, setting prices and quantities are achieved this way.

One trader shouts out the price he is willing to sell at, while another shouts the price he is willing to buy at. The last price shouted amidst the climax of noise and movement just before the bell rings is the deal that is settled upon.

I notice some LME information packs on a ledge, which have been left here for guests. I read:

Welcome to the London Metal Exchange (LME). In this place weight is king, the heavier the better; the more you weigh, the more chance you've got of getting one over in the ring. In fact, here at LME we expect our most senior traders to be obese. Our employees are lightweights when they arrive, often as school leavers, but they soon learn to punch above their weight.

On arrival all LME traders get to choose a character profile for themselves. This profile is based on the imagined physiological/psychological characteristics of a single metal or combination of metals such as: copper, lead, zinc, aluminum, nickel, tin and steel. It takes years of trading and training to build up enough muscle strength to be able to carry the bodyweight of a fully qualified trader. Some traders choose to increase their weight with padding and armour (metal of course) while others prefer the simple gluttony of overeating.

Corrosion, fatigue and meltdowns are problems that all our traders face in their working lives. LME follows the 'Shine at Work'™ code for employees and has set up its own 'On The Scrap Heap' charity for Mental Metal Traders (MMT), who have encountered stress and fatigue in the workplace.

The paradox that the more power the traders had, the heavier they became, did not escape me. Continuing to watch, I become absorbed by each of the trader's performances in the ring. Every five-minute-long trading session has a natural curve: a tentative beginning that inevitably transforms itself into a climactic, deal-breaking end. Viewed through the frame of the gallery windows, the image of the traders is filmic, stark and theatrical. Grimacing, laughing, fighting and flirting with deft craft, they trade round after round; their personas and bodies visibly transforming as each deal is made. One trader puffs himself up with angry aggression; another hides his competitive know-how behind a cool, detached exterior; other figures stand on the fringe of the ring, weighing up gains and losses before committing to a position. Jubilation, relief and disappointment are all present. I feel the pulse of the trader's excitement and their disappointment and anguish too. I do not understand what is being traded, but this does not matter because the simple act of watching leaves me feeling exhilarated.

APOCALYPSE KETTLE

On my way back from the London Metal Exchange, I find myself outside another exchange: the Royal Exchange, the original exchange in the City of London, now transformed into a luxury shopping centre. I sit on a bench with a take-away cup of tea in a branded paper cup. It is 5.30pm. While sipping tea, I remember the spring day I spent here a couple of years ago protesting against taxpayers handing over money for the banking crisis. The protest was staged using the metaphor of the Four Horsemen of the Apocalypse. Four blocks of protestors led by four different horse effigies, starting at either Liverpool Street, Cannon Street, London Bridge or Moorgate railway station, made their way to the junction between the Bank of England, the Royal Exchange and Mansion House. The blocks represented four different apocalyptic visions: war, climate chaos, money crimes and homelessness. The date was 1 April 2009, otherwise known as 'financial fools day' or G20.[1]

Joining a horseman of war, I travelled the short distance from Liverpool Street train station in the east of the City of London to the Bank of England where other protestors who had also followed their apocalyptic visions were meeting. I remember how I stood in the middle of a crowd near this very spot. There were few City workers around that day; the ones who were there could only be glimpsed in the offices above as they looked

1 ... G20 protests erupt ahead of London summit ... Protestors take action in City of London ... Much protesting peaceful ... Some bloody skirmishes between police and protestors ... Thousands of people kettled ...

down on the apocalyptic carnival passing their double-glazed floor-to-ceiling windows. Some City workers held up twenty-pound notes, jeering as we walked by. We, the protestors, held up placards.[2] City workers had been told to dress down so they couldn't be identified and we had chosen to dress up. Our dress code was banker with a twist of caricature and theatrical pizzazz: pinstripe suits, pearls, tiaras, feather boas, false moustaches, make-up and masks. In the masquerade that played out that day, protestors presented as bankers while bankers tried not to look like bankers at all.

There were many artists there. A friend and I recently recalled seeing seven, excluding ourselves. I have a clear memory of a Spanish artist sat in the middle of the crowd painting the whole scene on a very large canvas.

Caught up in the carnival atmosphere, I didn't pay attention to the rows of police and police vans closing off the streets behind us. It wasn't until I decided to leave the demonstration that I realised I was kettled and had been for some time. The now nationalised RBS Bank had been ransacked after having its windows smashed and the kettle had started to whistle.[3]

I needed to get out, but each time I approached a police line with a request to leave I was told to try elsewhere, and each elsewhere I visited sent me somewhere else. Dizzy and trapped, I eventually found a sympathetic policeman who let me through the lines. I had found my elsewhere and got out, but not before the police Forward Intelligence Team had photographed me for their records.

After leaving the kettle at the Bank of England, I visited Climate Camp, another G20 protest in the Square Mile. Climate Camp had set up a campsite on Bishopsgate. Tents had been erected in the middle of the road; there was bunting and a sign which read: NATURE DOESN'T DO BAILOUTS! People were

2 ... The beginning is nigh ... You are revolting ... Resistance is fertile ... Stop trading with our future ... Housing is a right not a privilege ... o percent interest in others ... Bail me out Darling ... Mr Brown stop the banks shitting on us ...

3 ... Demonstrators kettled for up to seven hours ... Metropolian Police officers at highest level unaware of legal criteria for using tactic ... No toilets or water provided ... Police role should be to facilitate and not suppress non-violent protest ... Allegations made that Metropolitan Police used agents provocateurs during demonstrations ...

picnicking, making tea, talking and singing; an idyll compared to the scrum I had just left outside the Bank of England. It felt more like a fete than a protest, with police performing the role of community officers. Later that evening tactics changed when police stopped people leaving or entering the gathering and kettled Climate Camp too.

The next day I read that a man, a newspaper vendor who was on his way home from work, had died from a heart attack at the protest. His name was Ian Tomlinson. Only later did it become apparent that he had not simply died of a heart attack but had been struck by a police baton.[4] The police had immediately denied charges of misconduct until a video was presented showing Ian Tomlinson being hit from behind and falling to the floor in an unprovoked attack.

A week later, I returned to the City to take part in a memorial march for Ian Tomlinson from Bethnal Green Police station to the City of London. The group that gathered outside Bethnal Green station were subdued. We marched slowly down Bethnal Green Road toward the City beneath a black banner, stopping for speeches and to lay flowers at the place where Ian Tomlinson died.

---

4 ... Ian Tomlinson struck to ground by police baton ... Initial police statement claims protestors impeded medics from helping Tomlinson ... Video footage of police officer hitting Tomlinson and lunging at him used as legal evidence against them ... Later coroner's evidence contradicts original coroner's report ... Manslaughter charges against police officer reinstated ...

RIOTOUS RAINBOW

It is not far to walk the straight line between the three exchanges Metal, Royal and Stock. I have decided to make my way to the London Stock Exchange in Paternoster Square in time to catch people having an after-work drink. When I arrive in the square, I will find a seat in a cafe and begin to listen to people's conversations, transcribing what I hear in my notebook.

Oh ... shit.
You get what you pay for.
It's only going to get worse.
Re-engineer it and put it back in.
Are you on the eleventh floor as well?
That's the game we are in at the moment.
Are you thinking about buying somewhere?
You have got to push the envelope a bit more ...
Can I ask if you have got a lawyer present today?
It just needs a good market. It needs a bit of momentum.
A lot of it is very difficult; there is a lot of alpha male stuff.
How much do you get if that is not too much of a problem?
My boss asked me to ask you, how are you bringing in your goals?
You have a meeting with people and you know exactly what is happening, and then ... stuff happens.

Light rain starts to fall and a rainbow appears. It is August.[1] The evening air is electric; the moist atmosphere of rain and light has created the perfect conditions for the biggest and brightest rainbow ever to be seen. The rainbow emanating from the middle of Paternoster Square (next to the London Stock Exchange) spans over the City of London reaching the London Borough of Hackney. And in Hackney it is found shooting out of the top of a white van that has appeared out of nowhere and is parked in a road just off Mare Street.

The City traders are sitting outside the London Stock Exchange, enjoying an after-work drink despite the midges swarming around their heads. It has been a day from hell on the Stock Exchange and they need a drink to release some of the tension. America's credit rating had been downgraded, worldwide stocks and shares had plummeted and they had to salvage what they could.[2] The only certainty is that the crash is not going to go away, and the effects of it will be felt for many years. The debt crisis is here to stay; America is in debt, Europe is in debt, countries are indebted to other countries, some more than others.[3] At the moment it feels totally abstract: a bunch of numbers on a screen, the effects of which are incomprehensible, unimaginable even. Do the City traders enjoy the thrill of the collapse surrounding them? (I understand it may not be acceptable for anyone to openly admit this in public.) What about individual accountability? Had some of them lost personal money? Who had made money? Who was responsible?

For now, the traders' attention is not on the markets, but on the pot of gold they have just witnessed appear in the middle of Paternoster Square. Transfixed, they stand in awe of the glistening crock's beauty and brightness. Some of them have traded in gold but have never seen, touched or picked up a gold bar before. What is it doing here? Perhaps it is a corp-

---

1 ... Monday 8 August 2011 ... London in the grip of riots ... Markets fight off global recession ...

2 ... Debt crisis sends shares falling ... FTSE falls ... Financial world in crisis of confidence ... Unclear if drop is early warning sign of economic recession ... Dollar and Euro currencies face real problem ... US credit rating downgraded ... Red numbers cover screens at London Stock exchange ...

3 ... Global finance system interconnected ... Countries lend money to other countries ... Recession and inability to repay debt exposes lenders to losses ... Exposure to debt puts countries at risk ... Many countries owe each other money ...

orate treat? Unlikely, but there is no disputing that there is a pot of gold at the end of the rainbow![4] They had heard about pots of gold as children, but as adults they had come to realise that such things were folklore, myth, something no longer to be believed in. But here, before their eyes, is a glistening, golden pot with little bricks of happiness nestled inside. Perhaps this is a reward for all their hard work, something solid, that will not lose its value and which may make things a little more comfortable during the bleak days ahead.

Twenty City traders have now surrounded the pot and are waiting for something to happen. Experience tells them that a semi-clad woman could turn up with canapés at any moment. But what is really on all their minds is: who will dare to make the first move and take one of the golden bars?

Meanwhile, in Hackney, the white van that had appeared out of nowhere stands in the middle of the street with its doors open wide. It is loaded with brand-new trainers. The evening is just beginning. Protests (or riots depending on your political persuasion) are kicking off across the borough. These events in Hackney have been preceded by protests in Tottenham on Saturday night and disturbances around London on the previous evening. There is always something, a flashpoint that ignites and triggers another set of events. The spark this time was the police shooting of Mark Duggan.[5] The protests erupt.

The group mustering outside the van wonder where it has come from. Could it be a police trap? Inside the van, there are trainers in all sizes, and enough for everyone. A protestor was about to joke that this was a 'corn'ucopia for tired feet, but decided to keep the insight to herself.

Back in Paternoster Square, the City traders are getting more and more curious and greedy. They want some of the gold. After talking about rainbows and pots of gold, they decide they should take the gold before both it and the rainbow disappear. Since the pot of gold belongs to a leprechaun, who is not here and cannot claim it, the City traders believe it should

4 ... Nervous investors buy gold in uncertain market ... Gold prices go up then come down again ... Standard gold bars held as gold reserves by banks ...
5 ... Black and Asian youth more likely to be stopped and searched than others ...

be theirs for the taking.[6] One of them leans forward and picks up a gold bar. It is heavy. Soon others follow; each picking up one, then two, then more gold bars. Every time a gold bar is taken out, the pot produces another one and then another, and so the City traders take more and more, at which point a very strange thing begins to happen. As the City traders fill their pockets and bags with gold bars, they become lighter; the more weight they take on the nimbler they feel. It is a feeling that connects to the exuberance of the moment; they have just struck gold and are going to be rich(er).

The group surrounding the white van in Hackney is growing as people tweet, text and instant message their find. While some go in to get themselves a pair of trainers, others act as lookouts before going in themselves. Like the pot of gold, every time a pair of trainers is removed, another pair appears, and before long there are lots of people on the street all wearing new trainers. Once on, the trainers make their feet tingle. They feel light and giddy, giggly even, filled with the exhilaration of the moment.

At 6.40pm both the City traders and Hackney citizens find themselves floating above the ground, just a centimetre at first, then two, three, then thirty. The Hackney citizens adapt to their airborne status very quickly. They dance in the air, shimmy, perform high kicks and the occasional somersault in a zero-gravity dance-off. The City traders are more guarded in their response; they have no idea what is happening and remain rigid, holding onto their gold whilst trying to control their upward trend and return to the ground as soon as possible. The unpleasantness felt by the City traders is made worse by the increasing number of midges swarming around their faces, which they cannot brush away because their hands are full of gold bars.

What both groups do not realise is that the gold and trainers are causing them to elevate, and that they are about to be carried over the rainbow.

The Hackney citizens float on the upper red band of the

6 ... Leprechaun stores gold coins earnt from making shoes in a pot at end of a rainbow ...

rainbow, while the City traders are carried across on the blue band. What a view over London they have as they soar up into the evening air. At the rainbow's apex both the Hackney citizens and the City traders see each other for the first time. Face to face the twenty City traders and thirty Hackney citizens hover in mid-air over Islington. 'We are all in this together ...' say the City traders, and the Hackney citizens reply '... but some of us are more in it than others.' At which point they begin their descent. The way down, an electric slide to the ground, is much faster than the way up. The rainbow deposits each group on terra firma: the Hackney citizens in the City of London and the City traders in Hackney. At that moment it stops raining and the rainbow that has transported them so elegantly vanishes without a trace.

Stranded, a mile or so away from where they set out, the City traders find themselves in the middle of a street next to a burning van. The gold bars they have been holding in their hands and carrying in their pockets have turned to brick. Their leather-soled shoes are now trainers and their jackets, hooded sweatshirts. One of them has been stung on his brow by a bee and his eye is swollen, while the faces of the others are red, blotchy and scratched from midge bites.

Moments after they land, the police come round the corner and see what they believe is a group of twenty youths with hoods, bricks and trainers standing next to a burning vehicle. Calling for backup, they approach with caution. To the police the City traders look wild and out of control, probably desperate. Once backup arrives, they arrest the whole group, split them up and take them to stations across the capital.[7] The only eyewitness is a strange-looking, short man dressed in green, who tells them that he had seen the gang slide down a rainbow. He is sent away with a flea in his ear and threatened with arrest for fabricating evidence.

7 ... Bankers arrested in Iceland and Dublin for roles in financial collapse ... First Icelandic prison sentences handed down to bankers ...

And so it comes to pass that twenty bankers are arrested and will be tried for that evening's looting and rioting.[8] But what will happen next? Will they get off? I am afraid not. No one will believe their story, not even their own lawyers.

And the Hackney citizens? How do they get on in the City of London? Like the City traders, they are also transformed on landing. Their jeans and trainers are swapped for pinstripes and pearls, and the pot of gold in the centre of the square becomes a suitcase containing over 100 smiley facemasks ☺.[9] After putting on the masks, they run across the square to the steps of St Paul's Cathedral where they hatch a plan to create some mischief in the City. They will customise the smiley facemasks, making them into angry emoticons ☹ and put one on every statue in the City of London. They even find some sympathetic bankers who volunteer to help them. The next morning Britain's economic centre will wake up to a Big Society banking sunrise of anger.[10]

Mission accomplished, they begin the two-and-a-half-mile walk home. On the way, they hear the timbre of a lone melancholy voice drifting out of the front door of a pub and onto the street:

Somewhere over the rainbow
Blue birds fly
Birds fly over the rainbow
Why then oh why can't I?

---

8 ... Establishment turns on disenfranchised inner-city insurrection ... Rioters not bankers sent to prison ... Prison population hits record high in England and Wales ... Hundreds charged with rioting and looting held in custody ... Average sentence for burglary after August riots in 2011 is 14.1 months ... Average sentence for burglary in previous year is 8.8 months ... Political approval given to banks who have ruined economy ... Political scapegoats made of rioters ...
9 ... Smiley faces made popular by rave culture in the 1980s and more recently used as emoticons in texts messages and emails ... Adopted by Steve Bell in cartoon series 'This is a big society stick-up' ... Characters wearing smiley masks hold up the Big Society Bank ... Bank has no money, only bollocks ...
10 ... Initial capital funding for Big Society Bank (BSB) to be provided by money from dormant bank accounts ... Government aim for BSB to catalyse growth of a social investment market and generate hundreds of millions of pounds for charities ... BSB was renamed The Big Society Capital group (BSC group) and launched in July 2011 ...

Passing the open door, one of the group sticks her head in and shouts '… the bank of justice is still bankrupt and we still know what we are fighting for'.

X, Z & Y

My friend x has arranged for me to meet z at restaurant y at 8pm. z is an investment manager and I am hoping he might shed a bit more light on my experiences in the City. He has been an investment manager for a long time. I can't remember how long, but from what he tells me it is really long, longer than I would have imagined by the look of him. y, the restaurant of my choice, is a prison-themed restaurant, the only one in the country. It is run by waiters dressed as inmates in stripy jumpsuits, and its clientele consists mainly of workers from the City: bankers, traders, finance managers, analysts and accountants. The unique attraction of this restaurant is that after eating (while locked in a cell), customers can choose to pay their bill at either gun- or knife-point. What the well-heeled clientele do not know is that the waiters are ex-prisoners and this is social enterprise, a big society flagship restaurant providing therapy to prevent violent ex-prisoners reoffending.

Every time a waiter holds a gun to someone's head, or a knife at their throat, they are being watched by a supervisor who is overseeing this controversial form of exposure therapy. The theory behind the therapy is desensitisation: each time the waiter holds up a customer they will find the activity more and more banal, so removing any form of thrill-seeking desire which might cause them to repeat themselves in the future. The research is still being trialled and the therapy is not yet proven.

The proprietor-cum-prison-warden hopes to open a branch in every major financial district around the globe. Asked in a recent interview why he decided to open his first branch in the City of London, he responded, 'if you can't bring Mohammed to the mountain, bring the mountain to Mohammed'.

The general ambience of the restaurant is criminal den meets high-class eatery. Customers are locked in small cells and their prison-themed food delivered through a hatch. I chose the restaurant after reading a gushing review in the Times newspaper. The reviewer raved about the food, saying it looked like slops but tasted of nectar. The menu is simple: a prison tray (vegetarian or meat option) and a daily 'last supper' special. You can order whatever you want for the last supper option, but this has to be done a week in advance.

We order a prison tray each.

Bankers and financial speculators have been betting on food and I want to know what z thinks about this and the risks involved.[1] Before I have the chance to ask, z begins talking about the noun most often used to describe bankers: 'greed'. Continuing to run with his own associative thoughts on food, he says that recently when he mentioned his profession at a dinner party he felt hostility toward him instantly rise.

'There is a lot wrong with the banking sector', he tells me. 'The banking industry pays its staff huge percentages of all profits in bonuses and wages. Much more than any other sector.' Continuing, he says that, like him, there are lots of bankers who care about both customers and their own wider social responsibilities, but who are stuck in a situation where it is 'impossible for individuals to act entirely ethically. What the banking sector really needs is government regulation.[2] At the moment, politicians are just paying lip service, a lot of political hot air that won't come to anything.'

Our dinner arrives on a tray divided into sections: a clear soup starter, a vegetarian main course of nut roast, boiled

---

1 ... British hedge fund buys 240,000 tonnes of cocoa for £650m ... Price of cocoa rises 150% ... Investment banks accused of making profit by gambling on food ... Financial speculation in agricultural sector one of the causes of world food price crisis in 2007–8 ... One in seven people in the world are hungry ...

2 ... Banking commission makes recommendations ... Retail banks ring-fenced from investment banks ... Bank capital reserves should be higher ... Taxpayers should not be liable for future losses ... Depositors get money back before creditors ... Should also be made easier for customers to switch banks ...

vegetables, mashed potatoes (for me) and a porridge dessert, all standard fare but with a modern European twist. I think what a nice guy z is as I take a sip of my glacial mineral water that, according to its label, was bottled in the Arctic and guaranteed to be made from melted one-million-year-old ice.[3]

Soon it will be time to pay the bill. We have decided to share so we can both experience being held up; I have chosen to pay at knife-point, while z has opted for gun-point. As the waiter approaches and holds his knife to my throat, I make sure I look him steadily in the eye.

3 ... Sea ice retreats in Arctic ... Arctic ice melt creates opportunity for big business ... Shorter cargo routes open up ... Ice-free seas open up opportunities for new frontier oil; drilling for oil in the Arctic ... More drilling means more climate change ... More climate change means more ice melt ... More ice melt means more oil ... More oil means more profit ... More profit means more investment in oil ... More investment in oil means more ice melt ... More ice melt means more drilling (etc. etc. etc.) ...

CRISIS CABARET

After dinner with Z, I go to meet my friend C for a drink at 9.30pm. Looking for a suitable bar we pass a sign that reads 'Crisis Cabaret' and decide to go in. It looks fun. We try to buy two tickets, but are told, 'you are invited to pay on the way out'. Apparently they have a performance-related-pay policy.

We go in and sit at a small table at the back of a room full of people eagerly waiting for the show to begin. A waitress wearing a blue dress who has a beaming smile and large ears takes our order. 'A Kamikaze cocktail for me and a Zombie for my friend,' I say.

The programme notes tell us that this is a pop-up cabaret night featuring two acts: Bonus, a banker clown,[1] and Boom & Bust, a female comedy duo.[2] The front page of the programme supports a black-and-white publicity photo of Bonus. He has a broad smile, wide eyes and holds a bowler hat in the air at a jaunty angle. His hair is short, greying at the sides and receding from the front. According to the programme notes he has performed in banks all over the world (Goldman Sachs, Morgan Stanley, Merrill Lynch, Lehman Brothers to name but a few).

Boom & Bust, according to the programme, were formed in the early 2000s, but did not work together officially until

---

1 ... Bank bonuses obscenely large ... Banks subsidised by public ... Bonuses continue to be paid as banks fail ... A reward for socially destructive behaviour? ... Is discussion around bonuses smokescreen to wider reform? ...

2 ... Short termism fuels boom/bust cycles ... Respective UK governments champion financial sector over other manufacturing ... Financial sector accounts for 10% of UK GDP ... UK household debt high ... UK economy over-reliant on consumption ...

2008. They too have performed all over the world. Their recent touring show 'PIGS' (latterly known as 'PIIGS') received critical attention in Portugal, Italy, Ireland, Greece and Spain, and was covered in the global press.[3] In their publicity photo the duo stand side-by-side. Boom is tall and thin, her head haloed by a large fuzz of hair. In contrast, Bust is short and squat with large breasts. They both grin a lot.

The house lights go down and the show begins. A single golden follow-spot lights centre stage, and Bonus the clown walks joyfully into its glowing pool. Looking at his audience he says 'hello' before jauntily stepping out of the spotlight again.

Playing with light and shade as if it were an on/off switch that enables him to appear or disappear, Bonus steps in and out of the pool of light saying hello in as many different languages as he can remember. 'Zdravo' (Slovenian), 'Labdien' (Lithuanian), 'Hola' (Catalan) and 'G'day' (Australian). After exhausting all the spoken languages he knows he moves onto sign language: American Sign Language, British Sign Language, Austrian and Swedish Sign Language.

Carrying a bundle of paperwork with CONFIDENTIAL stamped on it in red ink, he hails invisible friends from across the room. In anticipation of a reciprocal gesture of friendship he holds out his arm, which remains in the air for much longer than is needed. He makes the noise 'Psssst' to grab the attention of his invisible friends. He smiles, nods and laughs constantly, often at the most inappropriate times. He searches both his own and the audience's pockets for a mobile phone. Finding one in someone else's pocket he walks across the stage while sending a text message, just before falling into the audience and scattering the confidential papers throughout the auditorium. Despite every sheet of paper being blank, Bonus embarks on their collection as if the documents were top-secret.

Climbing back on stage he walks to the other side with his hand in his pocket and mouth open. When he does not know how to respond to a heckler in the audience he whistles and

---

3 ... PIIGS: Portugal, Italy, Ireland, Greece and Spain ... Seen as pejorative term ... Use of term banned by some financial journalists ... Portugal owes most to Spain ... Spain owes most to France and Germany ... Italy owes most to France ... Ireland owes most to UK ... Greece owes most to France ...

shakes his head. He has a swagger and his shoulders move from side to side while he walks. The crowd love him. We clap and whistle wildly, shouting, 'Bon-us, Bon-us, Bon-us, Bon-us'. He loves us back and in response to our praise and adulation he cries clown tears, which shoot out of his face and soak the audience in the front row. As money begins to cascade down onto him from the rigging above he removes his fake gold cufflinks and throws them into the auditorium before taking a bow, voicing a deep and throaty 'thank you', farting loudly and leaving the stage.

The audience are in tears of laughter as the lights come up. Our waitress appears again, this time with a blue plastic bag full of pens and sheets of paper. She gives the writing tools to the audience and invites them to take part in 'a competition to write a job description for someone working in the banking sector'. C and I obviously want to win and work up the following exemplar:

Job title: Hedge Fund Manager.

Position: Second to none, Self-appointed Master of the Universe.

Job description: Selling stuff, investing stuff, making shit loads of money, coming to work every day, adding stuff up and sometimes subtracting and dividing stuff.

Essential characteristics: Not giving a shit, arrogance and greed. An explicit interest in short-term gains and money should be important to you. Lack of empathy combined with the ability to compartmentalise your emotions is essential.[4]

Desirable characteristics: Both living by the sword and dying by the sword. A Latin speaker.

Boom & Bust are due to start any minute and we are all buzzing with excitement. The auditorium lights go down and the soundtrack to the reality TV show Dragon's Den fades in. Boom & Bust step into two red pools of light in the middle of the stage. They stand next to each other, deadpan as they face the

4 ... Some banks allegedly used psychometric tests to recruit social psychopaths ... Characteristics apparently suit senior corporate financial roles ...

audience. Bust points to Boom's hair and shouts 'Boom!' and Boom points to Bust's chest and whispers 'Bust'. This is obviously their catch phrase.

While they wait for the music to stop Boom deftly picks Bust's pocket. When Boom looks the other way, Bust picks Boom's pocket and when Bust looks away Boom picks Bust's pocket. So the performance continues for some time. Each of them sets up a structure of complicity, taking money from the other while looking to the audience for laughs between pocket picks. Bust constantly flinches throughout her performance. We never see what or whom she is flinching from. Boom, on the other hand, preens herself as if constantly looking into an invisible mirror that monitors both her posture and behaviour. The game ends as they each slowly, and painfully for the audience, realise what the other is doing.

In the next act they talk about The City of London, its structure of wards, committees and livery companies. 'Livery companies are the collective name given to craft and trade associations in the City of London. Historically these were clockmakers, fan makers and launderers', says Bust. Next, Boom insists that the names of the livery companies need to be modernised and suggests updating them to make them more relevant to today's working environment.

BOOM: The Worshipful Company of Phone Hackers and Purveyors of Salaciousness.

Laughter.

BUST: The Worshipful Company of the Manipulation of Desire and Spectacle.

Laughter.

BOOM: The Worshipful Society of Dashed Hopes and No Future.

Silence.

BUST: The Worshipful Society of Technological Organisers of Mischief.

Laughter.

BOOM: The Worshipful Society of Those Who Live in the Wrong Postcode Catchment Area.

Silence.

BUST: The Worshipful Company of Profit, Perversion and Persuasion.

Faint laughter.

BOOM: The Worshipful Society of People Who Stand Around All Day Getting Really, Really Bored and Who Are Paid a Pittance For Their Trouble.

Silence.

BUST: The Worshipful Society of Invisible Cleaning Technicians.

Silence.

BOOM: The Worshipful Society of Coffee and Tea Technologists.   .

Silence.

BUST: The Worshipful Company of Betting, Hoodwinking and Blustering.

Silence.

The sketch is not being received well. The duo's timing is completely wrong; their gags are delivered too quickly and neither can sustain eye contact with the audience for long enough to build any trust. They know the show is failing and attempt to recover their performance by acting more forcefully.

Next, the soundtrack to TV series The Apprentice is played while Boom & Bust act out a scene in which their task is to collect as many objects as possible from around the room and put them in two cardboard boxes.[5] They take anything they can

5 ... Lehman Brothers collapses ... Images of employees leaving offices with possessions in cardboard boxes broadcast worldwide ...

get their hands on: drinks, bags, coats, mobile phones, lighters and even diaries go into the boxes. During this part of the act, Bonus the clown is moving amongst the audience lyrically singing, 'buuuubbleessss, bubbles, buuuubbleessss galore' while distributing bubble mix and wands. The audience's attention switches immediately to Bonus and his bubbles. Standing in the middle of the auditorium, Bonus starts to blow big round charismatic bubbles and we copy him.

Now the room is filled with the most beautiful spheres. We all blow harder and harder, but I get dizzy and, thinking I might collapse, put my head between my knees. As quickly as they begin the bubbles disappear and the room falls silent. Boom & Bust are back in the spotlight standing side by side. Bust sets off two fireworks from inside her bra. The audience startle. Mimicking our shock, Boom & Bust jump around the stage and fall over. They have suddenly become painfully unfunny and we, the audience, turn against them and begin a slow clap: clap, clap, clap, clap, clap, clap, clap. We want Boom & Bust to stop. But Boom & Bust have no intention of stopping; they continue doggedly.

One by one audience members begin to leave until there is no one left in the auditorium apart from club employees, Boom & Bust and Bonus the clown. Boom & Bust continue regardless.

On leaving, c and I are confronted by three large bouncer clowns who physically block our exit with their body mass. Each is wearing a black jacket, polo-neck jumper, gold chain and red nose. They are carrying buckets with 'Minimum donation £40' written on them. We think this is a joke, only to find out it isn't. We offer the bouncer clowns ten pounds each because that is what we think the evening was worth. But the bouncer clowns remain insistent, forcefully recommending that we pay the full amount each, if we want to leave. Slowly the penny drops, the cabaret is a scam.

A short while later, I remember that my diary and watch are still in the brown box that was handed round during Boom and Bust's act, but by then it is too late and the door is locked and everyone has gone.

CRISIS CABARET

BROKE

Day is over. No more light shed. Confused. Another worst. Stock overpriced. Markets crashed. *More drink.* Banks bailed out. Taxpayers money used. Cuts now hurting. More on the way. Making money from crash. More crashes. Bankers have feelings. People in the City have relationships. Trust is important. City is spick and span. Clean. Disconnected. Unreal. *More drink.* Psychopathic boils. Lancing. Deception. Little empathy. Toxic debt. Recovery, but when? *More drink.* Floor-to-ceiling windows. Pass cards. White shirts and ties. Behind doors. Spill. Exchange. Male dominated. *More drink.* Management. Guarded by dragons. Wards. Journalists, lawyers and bankers. Global shenanigans. Live by the sword and die by the sword. Make money. Lose money. Bonuses and rewards. *More drink.* More risk. Legalised gambling. Addiction and adrenaline. Smoking on the street. Boom and bust. *More drink.* Banks rule the world. Remote. Administration. Removed. *More drink.* Sense? None. Understanding? None? Hope? None. *More drink.* Equality? None. Power? Yes. What? *More drink.* Where? Here. When? Now. Stop. *More drink.* Carry on. Don't remember. *More drink.* Lost. *More drink.* Stop. Sleep. Stagger. *More drink.* Fall. Who? Getting ready. *More drink.* None the wiser. For what? *More drink.* One more thing to do. *More drink.* It takes me. *More drink.* I'm soaring. Flying. *More drink.* Yes.

It is dark and I am on my way home when I see Bust at closing time, head in arms, lying slumped in a hedge. It is the end of a long day as 'Self-Appointed Artist-in-Residence' in the City of London and now it looks like I will have to deal with a drunken comic con-artist. Bust is jabbering something about the debt crisis. I tell her that she will have to move, as it is not safe to stay where she is. She says that she has been following a lead, but the trail has gone cold. She pulls me close, and I smell the alcohol on her breath as she whispers in my ear: 'the rotten teeth are in the rotten mouth'. Though initially disjointed, her speech is incredibly lucid, a messy logical contradiction. Some would say she had been driven to distraction by recent events; others would say this was a manifestation of her own inner turmoil. I don't know, nor is it my business to judge, but she suddenly seems more sane than most of the bankers I had just seen. In fact, she seems less out of control than all of them.

The last time I see her she has jumped on the back of a rubbish truck and is waving her arms in the air as if wielding an imaginary lasso and shouting at the top of her voice, 'Chaos, get thee behind me … so long, suckers'. I think the rubbish truck she has mounted is heading for the rubbish transfer station at Walbrook Wharf. She does not appear to care where she is going: her head thrown back, her cracked laugh whistles through the empty city streets like a prairie wind.

BROKE

EPILOGUE

If the climate was a bank they would have already saved it.
Hugo Chavez, Venezuelan President
Copenhagen Climate Summit, 2009

Common was written over the summer of 2011. This short period of time encompassed a crash in global markets caused by the downgrading of American debt and turbulence in the Euro-zone. At the same time an insurrection started in London before spreading to towns and cities across Britain.

Paternoster Square is the site of the London Stock Exchange where traders in 'Riotous Rainbow' find a pot of gold. While writing this story, I imagined the traders to be workers from there. I was subsequently told that traders no longer work at the Exchange; no 'open-outcry' trading floor exists any more, only computers. A decentralised electronic exchange and hollow epicentre without humans, calibrated to maximise trade at record speed. This has left a suitable hole in my story.

On 15 October 2011, Occupy London Stock Exchange (Occupy LSX) began its occupation of the forecourt of St Paul's Cathedral in the City of London. Original attempts by Occupy activists to set up camp in Paternoster Square were stopped by police and the Occupy LSX camp was set up outside St Paul's instead.

During this period, the private land of Paternoster Square was under twenty-four-hour guard with a police van permanently parked on site. The square was filled with a labyrinth of metal fences to deter occupiers. When I visited in January 2012 both the sculpture Shepherd and Sheep by Elizabeth Frink and the Christmas tree were caught in this corporate art install-ation. Within the grid, the pastoral image of a shepherd and his sheep was transported to an industrialised landscape, watched over by traders instead of shepherds. This was not the bucolic image that the square normally projects. An official sign on the side of the fence read 'We hope to have Paternoster Square back to its best soon!'

At the site of Occupy LSX, I saw tents that were raised on pallets to protect their residents from the chilling winter ground beneath them and clothes hung out to air on surrounding fences. And what practical good fortune that the Occupy camp ended up next to a camping shop, Blacks. Blacks had just gone into administration with a debt of £36 million. If Blacks can write off £36 million by simply ceasing trading, why not write off all debt?

The summer's insurrection erupted from gaps between income, from inequality, disenfranchisement and oppression. For those living at the bottom of the wealth pyramid in Britain, things are getting worse as money haemorrhages from the public sphere into the private realm. Support for the un-employed and disabled is being cut. Libraries, galleries, sport and social centres are being closed. While hospitals are being privatised and essential support services replaced by charitable giving, the banks are being propped up. Eventually meeting the needs of citizens may no longer be the legal responsibility of government. This is a crisis.

I remember a woodland walk:[1] sun shining through the trees, its golden light caught on the wings of insects hovering in the evening air. The woodland was quieting for the night as a wren chirped in a nearby tree. Something was bothering her. This was not a song but a danger signal, which alerted neighbouring birds to an intruder. In turn the birds picked up her call and carried her message far and wide. Her warning, tweeted to protect

1 ... City of London owns and manages public open spaces in and around London ... These include amongst others: Epping Forest, Hampstead Heath, Highgate Woods, Ashtead Common, Burnham Beeches and South London Commons ...

herself and the other birds, was used collectively to stave off harm.

Well-kept woodland can be one of the most fertile eco-systems within our biosphere. Tall trees shade a moist wood-land floor of fern and brambles that in turn cover mosses and fungi. Bird droppings spread seeds and fertilise the soil, which is home to worms, insects and microbes. The soil gives back life to the woodland, which in turn nourishes the soil. Each species has its ecological niche amid the diverse flora, fauna and wild-life. But nature has her limits and the unlimited economic growth we are currently experiencing is also causing the extinction of plants and animals. For the future of our earth we must recog-nise the environment's limited capacity and work together to protect our global commons.[2]

Rapacious economic growth over the past fifty years has been accompanied by larg-scale ecological degradation. What were once rocks and minerals are now piles of toxic seeping waste. These finite resources are discarded and left to pollute. There cannot be unending growth in a finite world. The question is how can growth be slowed to protect our environment while also ensuring that people do not suffer or starve. An equal distribution of wealth would be a start. Sequestering profits made by multinationals and environmental polluters and curbing the excesses of the wealthy would fund investment in jobs that support a socially and environmentally just transition: insulating homes, installing solar panels, building energy efficient trans-port networks and sustainable food growing systems.

The small geographical square mile of the City of London is dissociated from and disproportionate to its destructive global impact; corporations plunder our world, pollute our air, water, bodies and land, and then charge us again to clean up their mess. We are told repeatedly, through the paternalistic warm blanket of advertising, that they are our friends. Irre-versible climate change, loss of human, animal and plant life,

2 ... Economy and ecology share the same prefix ... Eco derives from the Greek oikos understood as home ... Economy can, via oikonomia be understood to be household management ... Ecology is the study of the relationship of the organism to its environment ...

social injustice, war, the support of dictators are not accounted for by these corporations where performance is everything.

Finding my voice in the City, I assigned myself the role of an outsider looking in. And it is 'without the walls' that I remain as I write this epilogue.

EPILOGUE

GLOSSARY

A

Agent provocateur: an agent employed by the police or other agency to go undercover and incite or provoke illegal behaviour. Often used as a tactic to discredit the political aims of a group or individuals.

Andy Coulson (1968–): former *News of the World* editor and Conservative Party communications director (2007–11) who resigned because of his role in the phone-hacking scandal.

The Apprentice: a British reality television show in which young businessmen and women competed for a £100,000-a-year job working as an apprentice to magnate Lord Alan Sugar. In the later series they would compete for £250,000 investment in their own business.

B

Bank: takes money from savers and lends it to borrowers, making money from the differences in interest payments. Banks also create new money when they offer credit.

The Bank of England: the central bank for the UK. Most modern central banks have been based on the model of the Bank of England.

Bank Station: an underground station in London that connects the Central, District, Circle, Northern, Docklands Light Railway, and Waterloo and City Lines.

Barts and the London Hospital Trust: an NHS trust that runs the Royal London Hospital, Whitechapel; St Bartholomew's Hospital in the City of London and The London Chest Hospital in Bethnal Green.

Bethnal Green: an area to the east of the City of London, in the borough of Tower Hamlets.

Big Society: no one knows what the Big Society is. The term was coined by the Conservative Party for their electoral campaign in 2010, and has been used as an ideological carrot to get people to work for nothing, in jobs for which they would have previously received a living wage. The term is an appropriation of Civil Society.

Biosphere: all of the earth's ecosystems are considered to be a single self-regulating system.

Bishopsgate: a road in the northeast part of the City of London, and named after the gate, Bishopsgate, situated in the original London wall.

Bond: a contract of repayment that includes interest and a repayment schedule. A bond is like a loan.

Bonus: extra pay reward. Often awarded to bankers for just for doing their job.

Boom and Bust: an onomatopoeic cycle of rapid economic growth followed by a sudden contraction.

Building society: a mutual community of lenders and borrowers who pool their resources to offer financial services.

C

Canary Wharf: a major financial district in London, developed in the 1990s alongside the City of London.

Cannon Street: a central London underground station and railway terminus in the City of London.

Citizen: a member of a community such as a country, city or town.

City of London: the historic centre of London around which the modern capital was built. Often referred to as the City or Square Mile, the City of London is a major financial centre.

City of London Corporation: the municipal governing body of the City of London.

City of London Police: The City of London Police are responsible for the Square Mile and all corresponding bridges: Blackfriars, Millennium, Southwark, London and Tower Bridges. Amongst other duties, they are responsible for tackling economic crime.

Climate Camp (2006–11): a collective grassroots group dedicated to taking direct action on climate change and challenging government rhetoric and corporate spin.

ConDem: slang term for the Conservative and Liberal Democrat coalition government formed in 2010.

Conservative Party: a political party in the United Kingdom.

Copper: slang for 'policeman' or 'policewoman'.

Cornhill: a main street as well as a ward in the City of London.

Corporate Social Responsibility (CSR): a voluntary form of corporate self-regulation; an ethics applied to business rather than an individual.

Credit union: a financial co-operative that is similar to a bank, but owned by its members.

D

Deepwater Horizon: an offshore drilling rig that blew out in April 2010 causing the biggest offshore oil spill in US history.

Dragon's Den: a British reality television show in which entrepreneurs pitch business ideas to secure funds from a panel of venture capitalists.

E

Ecosystem: a system in which living organisms and the environment function together. In an ecosystem animals, plants, micro-organisms, rock, soil, atmosphere and water all interact.

Elizabeth Frink (1930–93): an English sculptor and printmaker.

Ethical bank: a bank that approaches the ecological and social impact of its investments and loans ethically.

Eton College: a private boys' school for ages 13 to 18. It is described as the most famous public school in the world.

Eton mess: traditional English desert of strawberries, meringue and cream.

Euro Millions: a European lottery draw that takes place twice a week.

F

Farringdon: an area in the City of London represented by the wards Farringdon Within and Farringdon Without (within and without the London wall).

Financial Fools Day: a demonstration during the G20 summit in the City of London on 1 April 2009. The byline for the day was: 'We won't pay for your crisis.'

Forward Intelligence Team: police officers who gather intelligence on the ground, often conducting overt surveillance of the public.

Four Horsemen of the Apocalypse: the four horsemen described in the bible represent: conquest (white horse), war (red horse), famine (black horse) and death (pale/green horse).

FTSE: an index of the 100 largest companies listed on the London Stock Exchange. Informally known as the footsie, the FTSE is an abbreviation formed from the initials of its two owners: the *Financial Times* and the London Stock Exchange.

G

G20: a group of twenty finance ministers and central bank governors, from twenty major economies (nineteen countries plus the European Union).

GDP: gross domestic product, a national measure of the market value of all goods and services in a country within a given period.

Goldman Sachs: a global investment banking, securities and investment management firm. In 2011 HMRC (the UK tax-collection agency) let Goldman Sachs off paying ten million pounds' interest on a failed tax avoidance scheme.

Guildhall Art Gallery: established in 1886, the Guildhall Art Gallery houses the art collection of the City of London Corporation.

GLOSSARY

H

Half a ton: slang for a fifty-pound note, where a ton is one hundred pounds and half a ton is fifty pounds.

Hedge fund: a hedge fund is a pool of money, managed by a professional manager, that is used to take bets on various investments, including shares, bonds, commodities and derivatives. They are unregulated, and can take much higher risks than other types of funds. They frequently borrow lots of money to 'leverage' their returns.

HMRC: Her Majesty's Revenue and Customs, formed in 2005 by the merger of the Inland Revenue and Her Majesty's Customs and Excise Department.

Hurricane Katrina: one of the most costly and deadliest hurricanes in the history of the USA. Hurricane Katrina struck in August 2005.

I

Investment manager: A professional who is paid a fee to manage financial assets on behalf of others. For example, a mutual fund investment manager manages the money that people put into a mutual fund.

Islington: a neighbourhood in the London Borough of Islington that borders the City of London.

J

K

Kettling: a police tactic for controlling large crowds during protests that involves corralling large numbers of people in the streets without food and water.

L

Lady Godiva: rhyming slang for a five-pound note (a fiver).

Leadenhall Market: a covered market in the City of London.

Lehman Brothers: previously the fourth largest US investment bank. It filed for bankruptcy in 2008 after losing billions of dollars on the mortgage market.

Leprechaun: an Irish fairy in the form of an old man who wears green or red and likes to create mischief.

Liberal Democrats: a political party in the United Kingdom.

Liquidity: the ability to buy, sell or convert an asset to cash without affecting its price.

Liverpool Street: abbreviation of Liverpool Street railway station, which is located in the northeast corner of the City of London.

Livery companies: trade and craft associations in the City of London are collectively known as liveries. They include modern livery companies such as The Worshipful Company of Marketors, The Information Technologists' Company, as well as the more traditional Worshipful Company of Clockmakers and The Worshipful Company of Fan Makers.

Lloyd's broker: represents clients who want insurance through Lloyds.

The Lloyd's Building: situated at 1 Lime Street in the City of London and home of Lloyd's of London. The Lloyd's building was designed by architect Richard Rogers and opened on 18 November 1986.

Lloyd's of London: the world's leading market for insurance and reinsurance.

Londinium: the Roman name for their settlement on the site of the City of London.

London Borough of Hackney: a borough in the northeast of London; the most southwesterly tip of the borough touches the City of London.

London Borough of Tower Hamlets: a London borough located on the eastern border of the City of London, and to the north of the river Thames.

London Bridge Station: a London railway terminus and London Underground station in the London borough of Southwark, south of the Thames and outside the walls of the City of London. Thousands of commuters arrive and leave work from this station daily.

London Metal Exchange: a metals derivatives market.

London Stock Exchange: an international stock exchange located in the City of London where shares of public limited companies are traded. It can be accessed by members from computers anywhere in the world.

London wall: defensive wall built by Romans around Londinium between about AD 190 and 220.

M

Mansion House: official residence of the Lord Mayor of the City of London, also used for some City of London functions.

Mare Street: a street in Hackney running north to south; the Hackney Empire and Hackney Town Hall are both on Mare Street.

Margaret Thatcher (1925–): the first female Prime Minister (Conservative) of Britain (1979–90). While in power she privatised public assets and deregulated financial markets to fuel economic growth.

Mark Duggan (1981–2011): 29-year-old black man shot by police as they attempted to arrest him in Tottenham, London, on 4 August 2011.

Merrill Lynch: provides services in the areas of wealth management, securities trading and sales, corporate finance and investment banking services. It was bailed out the by the Bank of America. Despite losing billions, Merrill Lynch paid out an estimated three to four billion dollars in bonuses ahead of its merger in 2009.

Moorgate Station: railway terminus and underground station in the City of London.

Morgan Stanley: global financial services firm serving corporations, individuals, governments and financial institutions. Morgan Stanley's borrowing from the US Federal Reserve peaked at one hundred and seven billion dollars in September 2008.

MP: Member of Parliament in the United Kingdom.

N

News of the World (NOW): a British newspaper that ceased trading on 10 July 2011 as a result of its role in the phone-hacking scandal.

NHS (National Health Service): a publicly funded health service in England. NHS Scotland, NHS Wales, and Heath and Social Care in Northern Ireland are the names of the devolved health services throughout the rest of the United Kingdom.

Northern Rock: a British bank, and the first in 150 years to suffer a bank run. It was the recipient of loans in 2007 and nationalised in 2008. Virgin Money bought Northern Rock in 2011.

Nugget: slang for coins.

O

Occupy London Stock Exchange (Occupy LSX): a non-violent occupation of the forecourt of St. Paul's Cathedral in the City of London in protest against economic inequality. The camp was set up in solidarity with Occupy Wall Street on the 15 October 2011 and was ended by police eviction on the 28 February 2012.

P

Paternoster Square: an urban development next to St Paul's Cathedral and home to the London Stock Exchange.

Paul Kelleher: a theatre producer who in 2002 decapitated the marble statue of Margaret Thatcher that was on display at the Guildhall Art Gallery. He was jailed for three months in 2003.

Penny: slang for a one-pence coin. Also a woman's name.

PFI (Private Finance Initiative): a way of creating 'public–private partnerships' by funding public projects through private capital.

PIGS: an acronym that refers to the economies of Portugal, Italy, Greece and Spain and which can also be known as PIIGS, to include Ireland. The term groups together European economies facing economic crisis. The term PIGS has been restricted or banned by some news and economic agencies for being offensive.

Q

Quantitative easing: money that is injected into the economy to stimulate it. This is achieved by the Bank of England purchasing government bonds from the institutions that hold them; in other words, giving people money in exchange for the bonds, thereby injecting the money into the economy.

R

RBS (Royal Bank of Scotland): a bank that was bailed out by the British taxpayer in 2008. It is one of many UK banks involved in bankrolling environmentally destructive fossil-fuel projects.

Richard Rogers (1933–): a British architect best known for the Pompidou Centre in Paris, and the Lloyds Building and the Millennium Dome, both in London.

GLOSSARY

The Right Honourable Lord Mayor of London: annually elected head of the City of London Corporation, the Lord Mayor's role is to promote and support businesses and people of the City of London.

The Royal Exchange: originally founded as a centre for commerce in 1565, the Royal Exchange is now a luxury shopping centre in the heart of the City of London.

The Royal London Hospital: a hospital in Whitechapel, east of the City of London and part of Barts and the London Hospital Trust.

S

Score: slang for a twenty-pound note.

Scotland Yard: headquarters of the Metropolitan Police, London.

Smiley: a yellow circle with dotted black eyes and a broad smile, currently used in popular culture as an emoticon (the pictorial representation of feelings through punctuation) to enhance a text message or other digital forms of communication.

St Bartholomew's Hospital: a hospital in the City of London, part of Barts and the London NHS Trust. Also known as Barts or St Barts.

St Paul's Cathedral: a cathedral in the City of London and seat of the Bishop of London.

Steve Bell (1951–): political cartoonist who works for the *Guardian* newspaper.

T

Tenner: slang for a ten-pound note.

Theresa May (1956–): a Conservative politician appointed Home Secretary and Minister for Women and Equalities (2010) in the Conservative/Liberal Democratic (ConDem) coalition.

Threadneedle Street: a street in the heart of the City of London. Home of the Bank of England, otherwise known as 'the old lady of Threadneedle Street'.

The Times: a British daily newspaper owned by News International (who also owned the now defunct *News of the World*.)

Tottenham: an area in the London Borough of Haringey, situated in the northeast of London.

Trader: someone who buys and sells financial products: stocks, bonds, commodities and derivatives.

Tube: London's underground railway system.

Tuppence: slang for a two-pence coin.

U

UK Uncut: grassroots movement that acts to highlight alternatives to government spending cuts.

Underwriting: a practice of insurance in which the eligibility of a customer for a mortgage, insurance or other financial product is assessed.

UNISON: Britain's largest public-sector union.

V

W

Walbrook Wharf: an operating freight wharf in the City of London. Rubbish from the City is collected here before being taken by barge to Essex.

Ward: The City of London is divided into twenty-five wards, the remainder of a medieval governmental system in which each ward could act as a self-governing unit. It is also the name for a hospital block for patients with a shared or specific condition: a hospital ward.

Water cannon: a device used to fire a high-powered jet of water that can be used for fire fighting and, more contentiously, crowd control.

Whitechapel: an inner city area in the London Borough of Tower Hamlets, located to the east of the City of London.

White paper: a report in which proposed changes to government policy are presented prior to legislation.

X

Y

Z

**Copy Press is committed to
bringing readers and writers
together and invites you to join
its Reader's Union – please visit
www.copypress.co.uk**